C. Thomson & Co., Ltd., 1996. Printed and published
mson & Co., Ltd., 185 Fleet Street, London EC4A 2HS.
ISBN 0-85116-618-0

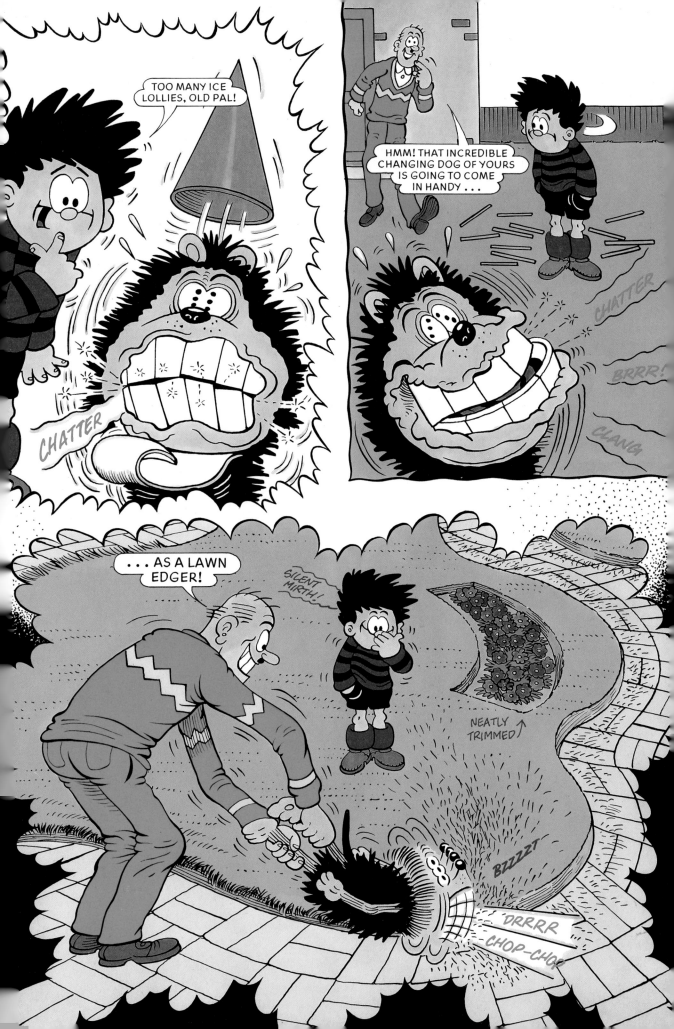

SNITCH and SNATCHY'S

Our AQUABEDS are water-filled.
They mould themselves to every build.
So comfy you could sleep all day,
Cos in these beds you'll want to stay.

My AQUABED proved quite a shock,
When on it nimbly I did flop.
Drenched was I from toe to head —
Which menace dared to prick the bed?

ZIPP SOCCER BOOTS are quick and light,
They'll leave opponents out of sight.
Every match your team will win,
So chuck your old boots in the bin.

ZIPP SOCCER BOOTS don't take to mud,
I snapped a lace and lost a stud.
My toes are covered now in blisters —
Give these disasters to your sisters.

THROB

ADVERTISING DISASTERS

TLE MISSY PERFUME'S very sweet,
flower whiffs it can't be beat.
s the fragrance of fresh roses —
y it on in massive doses.

LITTLE MISSY PERFUME will make you sick,
If you find some hide it quick.
It smells like very ripe manure,
I'm sure they filled it from a sewer.

FISS!

ANGY SAUCE is great on fries,
s up burgers and steak pies.
ze it, not a drop to waste,
etchup' on this super taste.

RED TANGY SAUCE is rather dull,
Like Steve Davis, clouds and Hull.
The only way it can be fun
Is loaded in your watergun.

RED TANGY SAUCE

SPLAT!

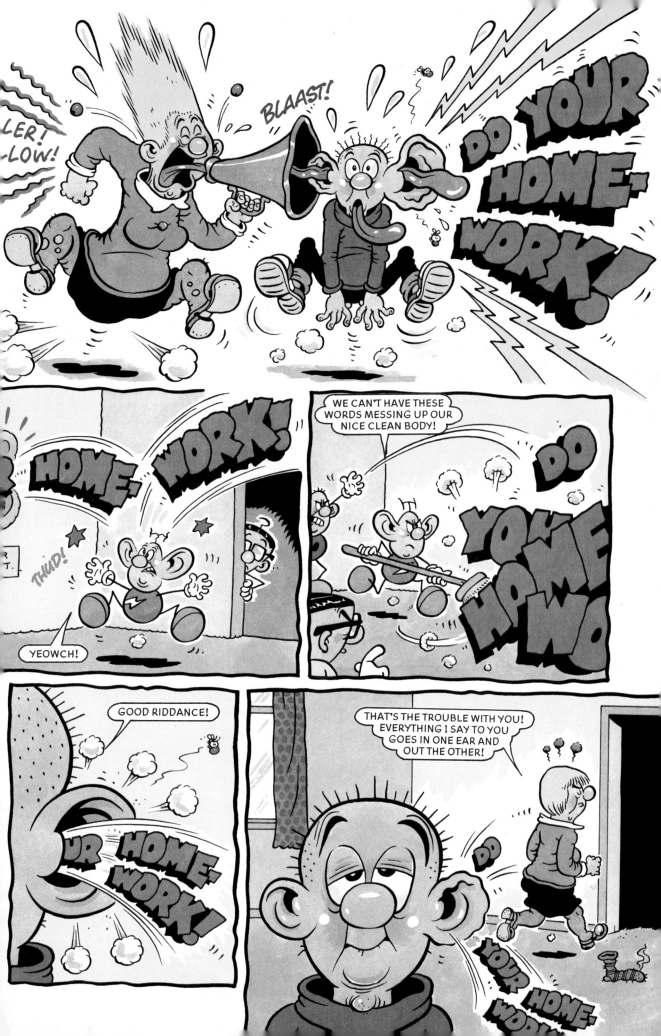

ULP! SOUNDS AWFUL, PASS!

MEOWL!

SPIT! GROWL!

YES! PASS!

NO — PUSS! WINSTON, THE BASH STREET CAT. I PUT HIM IN THERE HOURS AGO!

MEOWL!

YOUR MYSTERY GUEST, MINNIE'S TEAM!

FUME! PLOT! REVENGE!

DON'T KNOW!

I CAN'T SEE HIS FACE!

BUT WE RECOGNISE WHAT'S AHEAD OF HIM! A HERD OF RUNAWAY HIPPOS!

RAPIDLY RUMBLING RAMPAGE

IT CAN ONLY BE CALAMITY JAMES!

SPLAT!

CORRECT. NEXT ROUND, 'WHAT HAPPENS NEXT?'

A QUESTION OF BEANO

YOU GET A FACEFUL OF CUSTARD?

WRONG, TWO POINTS AWAY. WATCH YOUR MONITORS, DENNIS'S TEAM.

A QUESTION OF BEANO

GRANNY IS ON A MAZY DRIBBLE.

IT'S A FOUL! A PENALTY!

GNASHTY FOUL!

WRONG! THIS IS WHAT HAPPENS NEXT!

HOWL!

OOPSH!

LITTLE SOCCER BOYS"

EN LITTLE SOCCER BOYS,
L WERE PLAYING FINE.
NE UPSET A GREAT BIG GIRL,
EN THERE WERE NINE.

NINE LITTLE SOCCER BOYS,
ONE BELIEVED IN FATE.
A BIG BLACK CAT THEN
CROSSED HIS PATH,
THEN THERE WERE EIGHT.

SIX LITTLE SOCCER BOYS,
GOALIE TOOK A DIVE.
MISSED THE BALL AND
HIT THE POST,
THEN THERE WERE FIVE.

FIVE LITTLE SOCCER BOYS,
TRYING HARD TO SCORE.
JIMMY TOOK AN EARLY BATH,
THEN THERE WERE FOUR.

O LITTLE SOCCER BOYS,
ING LOTS OF FUN.
Y BLOCKED A SHOT,
EN THERE WAS ONE.

ONE LITTLE SOCCER BOY,
HAD TO RUN AND RUN.
ATE HIS TEAM-MATES'
HALF-TIME PIES,
THEN THERE WERE NONE.

ROGER the DODGER

And —

PUFF! PANT!

Then —

GASP! WHEEZE!

Also —

SPLUTTER!

RIGHT, KIDS — STOPPERS OUT!

EH? WHAT?

—RN—

NOW WE CAN PLAY WHAT WE WANT WHILE SANDY'S BUSY.

YEAH! BEACH VOLLEYBALL FOR ME.

COOEE, CHILDREN! WHERE ARE YOU?

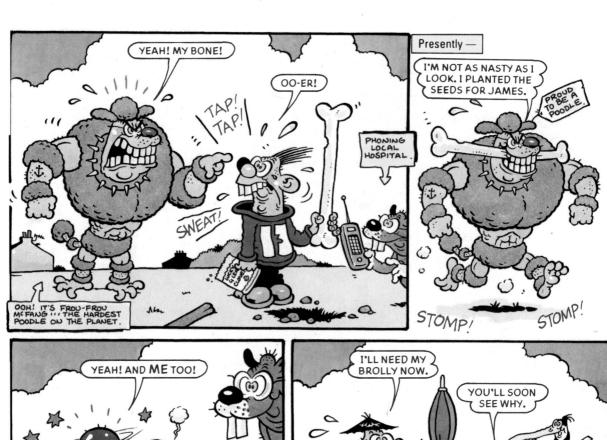

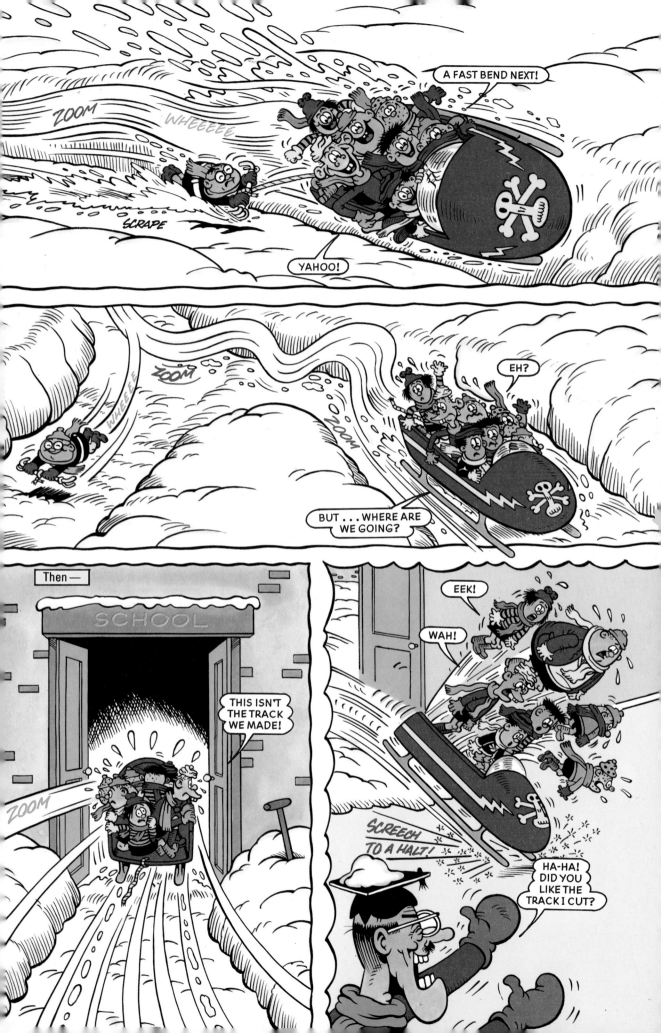

ROGER the DODGER
IN DODGING'S A PIECE OF CAKE

MMM! WHAT A GREAT SMELL.

WHO'S BEEN BAKING?

MY MUM. SHE'S A BRILLIANT COOK.

MUM WOULD GO WILD IF I TOUCHED HER CAKE, THOUGH.

YOU NEED A DODGE, MY FRIEND.

YOU CAN WASH ALL THE BAKING DISHES.

WOOPS!

ROGER! GRR!

TIME TO DODGE BACK TO COMIC LAND, I THINK.

MIND YOU, IT ISN'T EASY FOR TEACHER.

Teecher iz a nit!

RRINNG

WE'RE OUT OF HERE!

WE MUST GET RID OF THEM. BUT HOW?

AHEM! I'VE BEEN WORKING ON A LITTLE PROJECT AT HOME.

No peeping
TOP SECRET
KEEP OUT

The plot thickens!

WHISPER!
WHISPER!
FIENDISH PLOTTINGS!

EXCUSE ME! FANCY A SCHOOL TRIP?

YER!

BRILL!

MORE HARD SUMS
MATHS
JOTTER
HARD SUMS
HISTORY

SCHOOL BUS

DANGER! KIDS!
DO NOT FEED!

BEANO

SHRIEK! IT'S THAT LOT!

HELP!

HIDE!

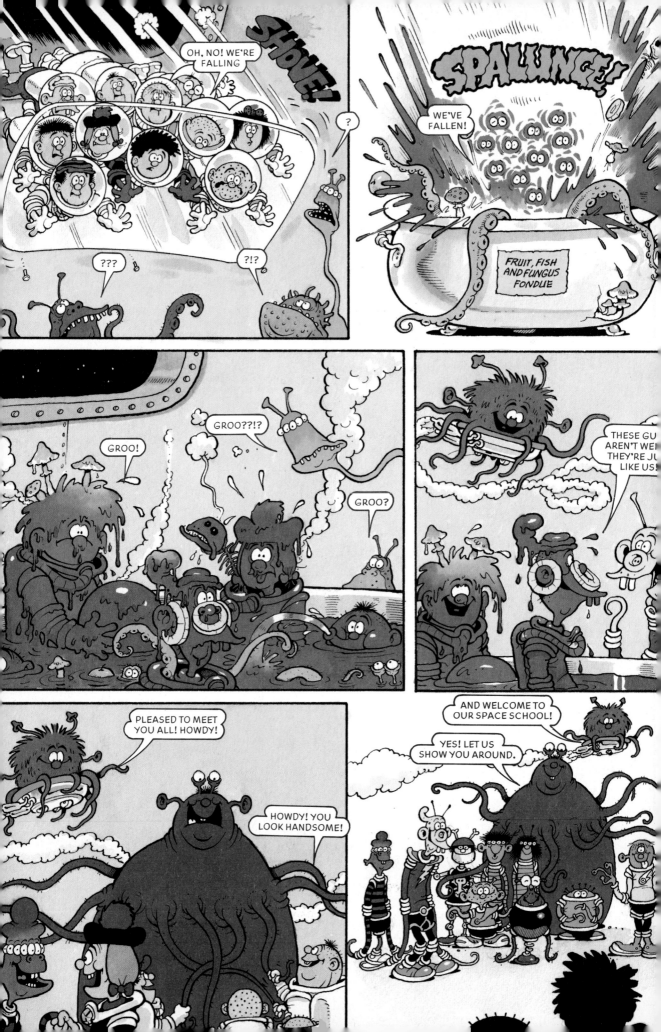

Gym class next.

I LOVE A GAME OF FOOTY!

ER, DON'T DO THAT!

BOOT!

OOFYAH! DO YOU MIND — MY RIBS!

ZIPPY ZINGDIZZLE OF ZODBANGER V — WHICH YOU'VE JUST MISSED!

ZZZIP!

AND MY WOTSIT!

HISTORY CLASS THIS WAY! IT'S MY FAVOURITE SUBJECT.

BZZZZ!

PRESS.

AND WHO WAS THE GREATEST HUMAN IN HISTORY?

NAPOLEON?

FZZAPP!

THAT'S HIM!

OR SHAKESPEARE!

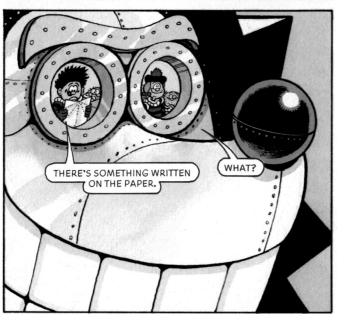

BANK ST. UNDERPASS

HOI!

POTHOLING PEST!

SORRY, LADS!

THANK YOU!

Then —

WELL, IF YOU WANT A REAL POTHOLING ADVENTURE...

...200 METRES THIS WAY...

...AND UP I GO!

NNNGH! I THINK I MUST BE NEAR HOME!

But —

SPLOOSH

WAA! A POND!

So —

BONK!

EH?

HO-HO! WRONG KIND OF POT!

IVY!

ZOOM!

YAHOO! I'M STILL POTHOLING!

HEH-HEH! POTHOLING IS FUN, BUT . . .

. . . IT DOESN'T HALF BUILD UP YOUR APPETITE FOR POT NOODLING!

POT NO

Make your own...

GARD

You will need...

A PAIR OF TIGHTS

GASP! MY TIGHTS!

SOME SAWDUST

CHEEK!
SCOOP

SOME GRASS SEED

SQUAWK!
SEED

A PING-PONG BALL

BOUNCE
SWISH
TUG

PLUS...
2 ELASTIC BANDS
2 SMALL PLANT POTS
A NEEDLE AND THREAD
A BLACK FELT-TIP PEN
DOUBLE-SIDED
   STICKY TAPE
SCISSORS

1	Snip the feet off the tights — watch out, this could be very smelly!	
2	Fill the "sock" with a spoonful of grass or watercress seeds.	
3	Add a few scoops of sawdust.	
4	Gather the ends of the sock so it forms a round ball.	
5	Secure the ends tightly with an elastic band.	
6	For the nose, cut out a circle (about 6cms in diameter) from the remaining tights.	
7	Sew around the edge with a running stitch - get Mum or a Softy to do this bit.	
8	Sew on nose. For eyes, cut the ping-pong ball in half and put on with sticky tape.	
9	Draw on the eye bits and the menace smirk with the black felt-tipped pen.	
10	Water until soggy. Place on windowsill. The hair will soon begin to grow.	

RDENING TIP...

'T USE FLOWER SEEDS
TEAD OF GRASS SEEDS,
ERWISE YOU COULD END
ITH A SOFTY —
UDDER!

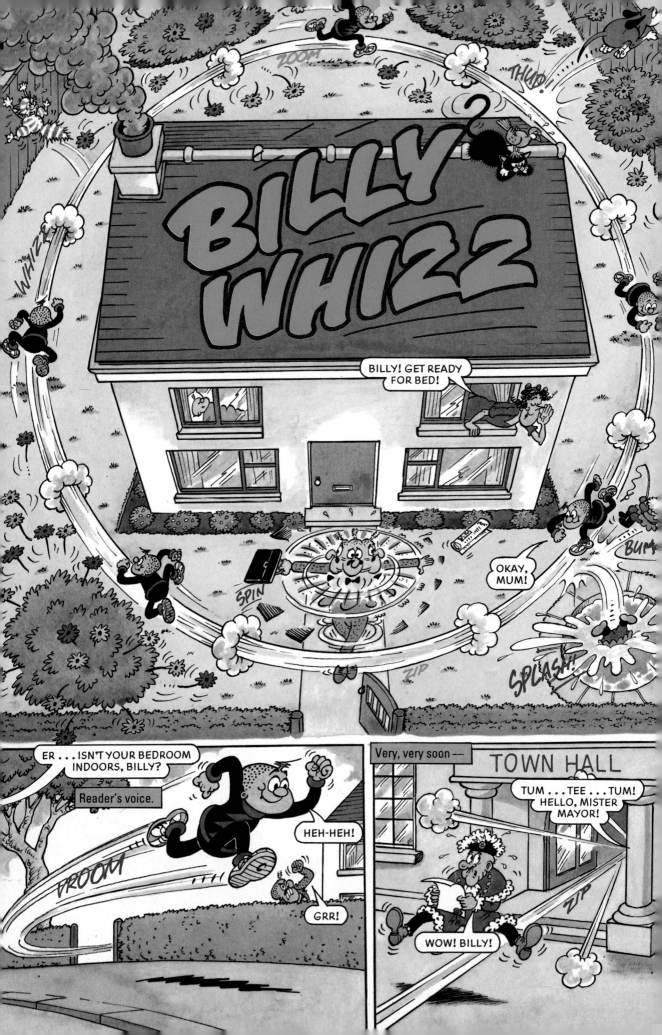

"Hi, hello!" said Sam the Slug.
"I've got such an ugly mug!"

"I'll dig deeply," said our slug.
"Into my giant savings jug."

So with a beep, burp and a chu
Off into town went Sam the Slu

Just then a pretty lady bug
Cast her eye on Sam the Slug.

"You really are a handsome sl
No longer do you look like Plu

face," said this poor lonely slug.
ks like the rear end of a Pug!"

"Wish that I could get a hug,
From a slimey female slug!"

to a shop slipped our young slug,
see the owner — name of Doug.

Soon out glided Sam the Slug.
Just see that grin — he sure is smug.

They set up home,
All warm and snug.
The secret?
Sammy's brand new rug!

LES PRETEND

I'VE REALLY BEEN LOOKING FORWARD TO THIS CANAL HOLIDAY!

BOARDING POINT

EDNA

LOVELY AND PEACEFUL!

HOWDY, FOLKS!

VIC VOLCANO

Shortly —

GOOD WORK, VIC!

GASP! PHEW! WHEEZE!

I THINK THE DOG NEEDS OUT NOW!

WHAT?

WOOF!

PHEW!

Soon —

HE NEEDS HIS EXERCISE, I SUPPOSE!

WOOF!

AHA! THAT SOUNDS AS IF THE DOG NEEDS TO COME BACK UP NOW, VIC!

HOWL!

EH?

SNARL! GRRR! I'VE HAD JUST ABOUT ENOUGH!

DRIP SWEAT

WE'RE BRINGING WILL OUT IN A COLD SWEAT! HA-HA!

GASP! WHEW!

Soon, at the Doctor's.

I'M IN A COLD SWEAT, DOC. CAN YOU HELP?

SCOOSH

HMM!

THIS WAY, WILL!

WAITING ROOM

Then —

THERE! MY PLANTS NEEDED A DRINK! CHORTLE!

HO-HO!

EH?

COO! I FEEL BETTER NOW!

'FEELING BETTER'! WE CAN'T HAVE THAT!

LET'S HAVE A GAME OF 'HIDE AND SEEK'!

HAR-HAR!

...10...11...12...

WE'LL HIDE!

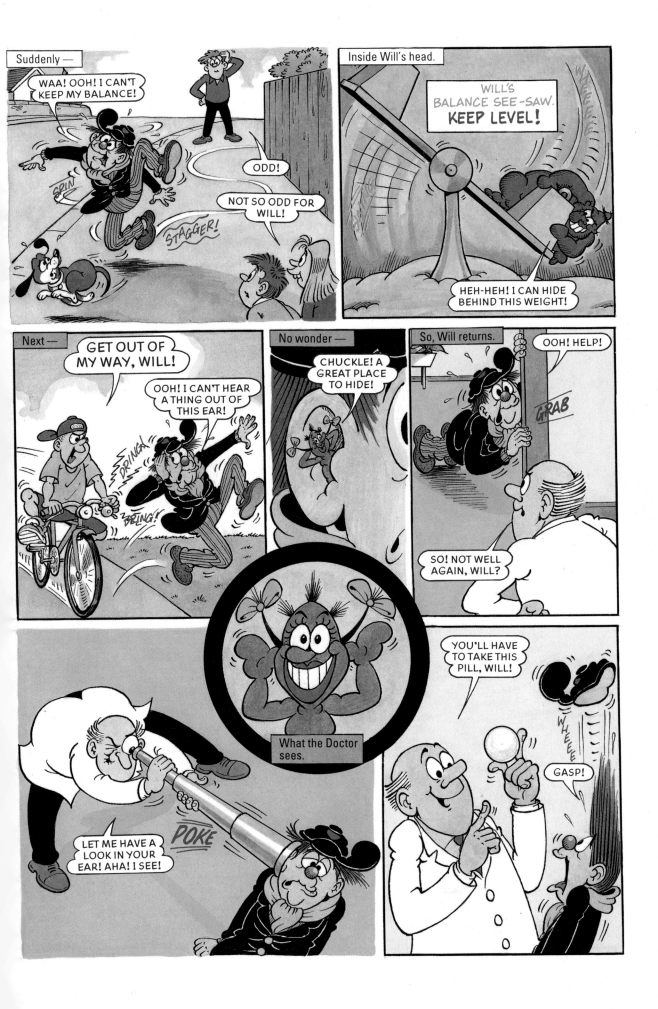

MINNIE the MINX

PEOPLE ARE USED TO THE FACT THAT I CARRY A WATER PISTOL.

SEE WHAT I MEAN?

I NEED A NEW WEAPON.

PSST! I CAN HELP!

EH?

COME IN!

MY NAME'S X — THIS IS MY SECRET WEAPONS TESTING LAB!

WHAT LOOKS LIKE A ORDINARY TENNIS BAL

THIS LOOKS LIKE A HARMLESS POGO-STICK . . .

. . . IT IS IN FACT . . .

And —

CHEWING GUM?

PHEW! THANKS!

But —

SNAP!

YEEOW!

NOT GUM — A SIM MOUSETRAP DEV

GNASHER- THE HISTORY
DOGGY LAUGHS THROUGH TIME
7 Gnigel Mansell
GNO STOPPING ME!
BUTCHER
VROOOOM!
RN-

So —

LET'S GO TO WORK!

The pals search hard —

Then —

GULP!

NO TREASURE — YOU DODGER!

NO . . .

. . . BUT PLENTY OF SCRAP METAL FOR THE RAG AND BONE MAN!

SCRAP

TINKER

TAILOR

SOLDIER

SAILOR

WHAT WILL JOE KING BE?

EL CHEAPO DOG FOOD is the best.
It's so much meatier than the rest.
It makes dogs want to run and bark,
And drag their owners round the park.

EL CHEAPO DOG FOOD'S really nasty.
I'd rather eat Dad's Cornish pasty.
It's so revolting it makes me howl —
EL CHEAPO DOG FOOD'S really foul.

PHOO!

GNASHER

OOF

New STRAIGHT UP HAIR GEL is so smart,
It makes you really look the part.
Out of place won't fall a hair,
Be your tresses dark or fair.

New STRAIGHT UP HAIR GEL is so greasy.
It really makes you feel quite sleazy.
Your precious locks this gel will alter —
It makes you look like Bert and Walter.

HAIR GEL

SPLOT!

ADVERTISING DISASTERS

Put SPOTLESS FACE CREAM on your dial.
If you're pimply it's worth a trial.
Why have acne, freckles or spots,
When SPOTLESS FACE CREAM clears the lot.

Using this cream's very simple.
It ridded me of every pimple.
It also took off skin galore —
Now I use it on the floor.

you're trying to lose weight,
ry SLIMMING BROTH upon your plate.
ou'll shed those pounds, it's guaranteed,
ith this delicious, hearty feed.

With SLIMMING BROTH upon my platter,
My big waistline just got fatter.
That thin soup was not much fun,
I soaked it up with fifty buns.

SLIMMING BROTH

FRESH BUNS

IVY The TERRIBLE

WE'RE DECORATING THE HOUSE! SO WE'VE COME TO BUY A FEW THINGS.

OH, JOY!

D.I.Y. SUPERSTORE

LET'S PICK SOME ROLLS OF WALLPAPER.

BATHROOMS
KITCHENS

FILLER

I SEE SOME!

AAIEE!

SHRIEK!

HOWL!

IS THIS ROLL BIG ENOUGH!

IVY! THAT'S A ROLL OF CARPET!!!

PAINT

WE'LL NEED SOME PAINT. THAT TIN AT THE TOP.

IT'S PRETTY HIGH UP.

EEK! A H-H-H-HEAD!

HIYA! NICE PAINT!

PAINT

PAINT

PAINT

YIKES!

WOW!

So —

WE'VE GOT EVERYTHING. LET'S GET CRACKING!

D.I.Y. SUPERSTORE

I'VE SET UP THE PASTING TABLE, DAD. PUT THOSE HEAVY ROLLS DOWN.

THANKS.

SNAP!

OOOO!

OH, DEAR! I MUST HAVE SET IT UP THE WRONG WAY. ACCIDENTS DO HAPPEN! NOW, I'LL PASTE THE PAPER!

IVY! NO! NOT THAT KIND OF PASTE! STOP!

IT'S FISH PASTE!

WAHEY!

SLOBBER!

GRUB'S UP!

SHOO! GERROUT! GO! VAMOOSE!

I'LL STICK UP THE PAPER.

THERE! A LOVELY JOB, ISN'T IT?

OH, ME! OH, MY!

THE BASH STREET KIDS

ZZZZ . . .

WE'RE GOING ON A CLASS OUTING TO THE SCIENCE FAIR.

HUH! NO CHANCE!

UNTIE

'BYEE!

LIFT

WAVE

WAVE

'BYEE!

HEH-HEH! THIS IS ONLY ONE OF THE NEW INVENTIONS YOU CAN SEE AT THE SCIENCE FAIR.

ERK!

PRESS

CLICK

BYOING

WHIRR

ZOOM

GRAB

EH?